SOBER STARTS TODAY

100 DAY SOBER JOURNAL

Lisette Paris Journals

How to use this book

Congratulations! You've made the fantastically positive decision to be alcohol-free for 100 days (or, who knows, maybe even longer). Maybe even for always. Something has brought you to this point. It may simply be a nagging sense that you've been overdoing it lately and could do with a break, or it may be that you are starting to worry about how often you're thinking of that glass of wine at the end of every day. Maybe you are feeling ashamed of hiding how much you are drinking, or maybe you've hit rock bottom. It doesn't matter what brought you here. This journey is for everyone, and going alcohol-free will benefit you - whether it's for now or for ever.

In this book, you will find 100 journal pages to help you track your alcohol-free journey day by day. But because giving up isn't easy, it is also full of information, distractions, ideas, planners, trackers and suggestions for delicious alternatives to alcohol.

Every week, you will find seven journal pages with inspirational quotes, a page for your weekly reflection, and a mocktail of the week to try (recipe quantities are for two glasses). As well as that, the first month gives you a week-by-week description of what to expect. There are regular pages for doodling, colouring, thinking and planning. You could even write down your own mocktail recipes! There are also monthly mood tracker charts, and weight loss and savings trackers to keep you motivated, as well as information on supplements, sleep and even herbal teas.

You can use as many or as few of the resources as you like. This journal is for YOU to design your own alcohol-free journey in whatever way works best for you. Good luck!

love Lisette

Contents

Mocktail recipes

Day ___

Today's goal

I struggled with

I succeeded in

Instead of drinking, I ___

Tomorrow I plan to ___

Today, I'm grateful for

What to expect in week 1

It takes just one hour for your liver to start clearing the alcohol from your system, converting it first into acetaldehyde. Acetaldehyde is a highly toxic carcinogen which causes nausea and tremors, and may also cause your pancreas to become overactive, spiking your insulin so that you crave carbs.

After 24 hours your blood sugar should normalise, but your body is still likely to miss the sugar boost alcohol gives you. Try to avoid binging on sweets and sugary drinks at this stage; drink lots of water and eat as healthily as you can.

The worst should be over within 3 days, but you can expect to feel tired and anxious. You may sweat profusely, feel shaky, or find your pulse racing. Headaches often hit with a vengeance around Day 5. The first week can be tough - but by the end of week 1 the physical symptoms will have passed. You are over the first hurdle!

How I'm feeling

_____

_____

_____

_____

_____

Day ___

Today's goal

I struggled with

I succeeded in

Instead of drinking, I _____

Tomorrow I plan to _____

Today I'm grateful for

Monthy mood tracker

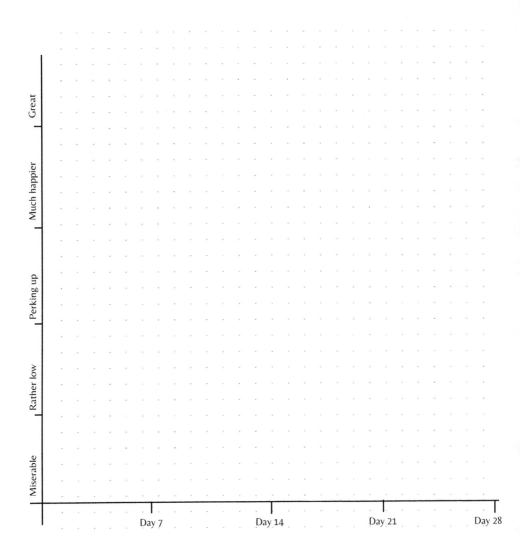

Great

Much happier

Perking up

Rather low

Miserable

Day 7   Day 14   Day 21   Day 28

Day ___

Today's goal

I struggled with

I succeeded in

Instead of drinking, I _____

Tomorrow I plan to _____

Today I'm grateful for

More reasons to be cheerful

Day ___

Today's goal

I struggled with

I succeeded in

Instead of drinking, I ___

Tomorrow I plan to ___

Today I'm grateful for

Day ___

Today's goal

I struggled with

I succeeded in

Instead of drinking, I _____

_____

_____

_____

_____

_____

_____

Tomorrow I plan to _____

_____

_____

_____

Today I'm grateful for

Weekly Reflection

_____

_____

_____

_____

_____

_____

_____

_____

_____

_____

_____

_____

_____

_____

_____

_____

_____

_____

_____

_____

_____

> The journey of one thousand miles begins with the
> first step.
>
> _Lao Tsu_

A nice cup of tea

Herbal teas or tisanes have all sorts of health benefits that can help you reset your body while you move away from your drinking habits. They are caffeine-free and delicious, too!

CHAMOMILE tea is best known for its calming and relaxing effects. If you're suffering from insomnia, this is the one to try. It is also believed to have anti-inflammatory, anti-bacterial and liver-protecting effects.

PEPPERMINT tea is used around the world both for its wonderful flavour and its health benefits. It is effective in aiding digestive tract health (so is another good one for the early days), but it also has anti-bacterial, anti-viral and anti-oxidant properties.

GINGER tea is a spicy, vibrant drink with excellent anti-nausea properties. It also stimulates the immune system and is an effective anti-inflammatory.

SAGE tea is well known for its medicinal properties. Studies have shown it may promote improvement in cognitive function, memory and mood.

ROSEHIP tea is high in vitamin C and antioxidants. Its anti-inflammatory properties may reduce inflammation and studies have also found rosehip effective in preventing skin ageing and reducing stomach fat.

There are hundreds more to try – so why not use your 100 days to enjoy experimenting?

Day ___

Today's goal

I struggled with

I succeeded in

Instead of drinking, I ___

Tomorrow I plan to ___

Today I'm grateful for

What to expect in week 2

You should now be sleeping noticeably better. Alcohol might make you fall asleep easily, but you probably wake up every night around 3am (you do, don't you?). Alcohol-induced sleep skips the important REM (rapid eye movement) phase of the sleep cycle, resulting in disrupted sleep. Poor quality sleep causes imbalance in the hormone levels that control our eating, as well as reducing our problem-solving capacity and emotional control. Sleeping better is a huge benefit of giving up drinking.

Your skin should also be looking much fresher and more hydrated. Alcohol is a diuretic that causes you to lose four times as much liquid as you consume, resulting in severe dehydration. Your skin should also be much clearer, as it no longer tries to expel toxins through the pores.

If you suffer from acid reflux, this will have also reduced, and by the end of week 2 your stomach lining will have repaired itself and returned to a healthy condition.

How I'm feeling

_____

_____

_____

_____

_____

_____

Day ___

Today's goal

I struggled with

I succeeded in

Instead of drinking, I _____

Tomorrow I plan to _____

Today I'm grateful for

Mocktail of the week

Rosy Glow

This pretty pink mocktail is bit of a girly treat, but I love the delicate colour and scent of roses.

2 teaspoons of rose water
Juice of two lemons
Squeeze of honey (to taste)
A generous splash of pomegranate juice
Top up with sparkling water

Combine all the ingredients except the sparkling water and pour over ice. Top up with sparkling water and garnish with rose petals. If you have time to plan ahead, try freezing pomegranate seeds (did you know they are really called "arils"?) inside the ice cubes for a special decorative touch.

Day ___

Today's goal

I struggled with

I succeeded in

Instead of drinking, I _____

Tomorrow I plan to _____

Today I'm grateful for

Relax and colour

Day ___

Today's goal

```



```

I struggled with

```


```

I succeeded in

```


```

Instead of drinking, I _____

_____

_____

_____

_____

_____

_____

Tomorrow I plan to _____

_____

_____

_____

Today I'm grateful for

```



```

Doodle and plan

Day ___

Today's goal

```

```

I struggled with

```

```

I succeeded in

```

```

Instead of drinking, I _____

_____

_____

_____

_____

_____

_____

Tomorrow I plan to _____

_____

_____

Today I'm grateful for

```

```

Health and vitality

Certain vitamins and minerals are likely to be lacking in anyone with a significant drinking habit. In addition to taking a good quality multi-vitamin-mineral supplement daily, the following supplements are often recommended:

- Alcohol interferes with the body's capacity to assimilate Vitamins B1, B3, B5, B6 and B12. A good Vitamin B complex will help replenish these as you start your alcohol-free journey.
- Vitamin C deficiency can cause tiredness and low mood, as well as making you more vulnerable to colds and flu. Taking extra Vitamin C can help minimise these risks and effects as well as boosting your anti-oxidant levels.
- Vitamin D3 is often very low in people who drink a lot. This vitamin assists kidney function, helping the blood maintain the correct ph level. It can reduce fatigue, depression and stress. The best source of Vitamin D is sunlight.
- Magnesium is responsible for the activation of around 300 enzymes and is crucial for bodily function. Alcohol reduces the amount of magnesium available to the cells and can cause fatigue, insomnia, cramp, anxiety and irregular heart rhythm.
- Omega-3 supplements are highly beneficial in assisting with brain tissue regeneration and nervous system function. Natural sources included oily fish.
- Milk thistle is an extract of the seeds of a flowering plant in the daisy family and has been shown to stimulate regeneration of liver cells. It is found in most health food stores as milk thistle, silybum or silymarin.

Please note, this book is not a replacement for discussing any health concerns around giving up alcohol with your own doctor.

Day ___

Today's goal

```
┌─────────────────────────────────────┐
│                                     │
│                                     │
│                                     │
└─────────────────────────────────────┘
```

I struggled with   *I succeeded in*

```
┌──────────────────┐    ┌──────────────────────┐
│                  │    │                      │
│                  │    │                      │
│                  │    │                      │
└──────────────────┘    └──────────────────────┘
```

Instead of drinking, I _____
_____
_____
_____
_____
_____
_____

Tomorrow I plan to _____
_____
_____

Today I'm grateful for

```
┌─────────────────────────────────────┐
│                                     │
│                                     │
│                                     │
└─────────────────────────────────────┘
```

Day ___

Today's goal

[ ]

I struggled with   *I succeeded in*

[ ]   [ ]

Instead of drinking, I _____

_____
_____
_____
_____
_____
_____

Tomorrow I plan to _____

_____
_____
_____

Today I'm grateful for

[ ]

Weekly Reflection

_____

_____

_____

_____

_____

_____

_____

_____

_____

_____

_____

_____

_____

_____

_____

_____

_____

_____

_____

_____

_____

_____

> Success is the sum of small efforts repeated day in
> and day out.
>
> _Robert Collier_

What to expect in week 3

By week 3, you should have started to lose some weight. Alcohol is empty calories and if you were drinking half a bottle of wine a night, you will have reduced your intake by around 2,000 calories a week (the equivalent of 5 slices of cake). And perhaps there were nights when it was more than half a bottle?

Your blood pressure will now also have gone down, significantly reducing your risk of stroke and heart attack. Your vision will be better, and your kidney function will have greatly improved. Week 3 brings important benefits for your long-term health.

How I'm feeling

_____

_____

_____

_____

_____

_____

_____

_____

_____

_____

_____

_____

Day ___

Today's goal

I struggled with   I succeeded in

Instead of drinking, I _____

Tomorrow I plan to _____

Today I'm grateful for

Good night, sleep tight

One of the great benefits of giving up alcohol is that your sleep will improve. Alcohol may make you drop off quickly but it also results in poor quality sleep. It affects production of the hormones that trigger sleep, causing them to subside too rapidly and leading to wakefulness. Alcohol also blocks the restorative REM sleep phase and increases alpha activity in the brain, distrupting sleep and leaving you generally unrested and unrestored.

Although insomnia can be a side-effect of the early days of alcohol withdrawal, a few things will help reset your sleep patterns:

- Drink a sleep-promoting herbal tea such as chamomile before bed.
- Avoid caffeinated drinks after mid-afternoon. Coffee is the obvious suspect, but caffeine is also found in black tea, hot chocolate and cola.
- Avoid screen time in the run-up to sleep. Try a book, podcast or soothing music instead.
- Establish a relaxing pre-sleep routine – whatever works for you. A bath or shower, stetching exercises or meditation are all good.
- Make your bedroom a restful environment, keeping external light and noise to a minimum if possible.
- Aim for a consistent sleep pattern, going to bed and waking up at around the same time every day.

Soon none of this will be necessary. You will be naturally tired at the end of the day, sleep soundly and wake refreshed!

Day ___

Today's goal

I struggled with

I succeeded in

Instead of drinking, I ___

Tomorrow I plan to ___

Today I'm grateful for

Mocktail of the week

Virgin Mary

A classic - mocktail or otherwise - and definitely one of your five-a-day!

200 ml tomato juice
Juice of half a lemon
A few generous dashes of Worcestershire sauce
A few drops of Tabasco sauce
Basil or celery leaves
Lime

Combine the juice and sauces and pour over ice in a tall glass. Garnish with torn basil leaves and a slice of lime, and add a celery stick to swizzle it all around.

Day ___

Today's goal

I struggled with

I succeeded in

Instead of drinking, I _____

Tomorrow I plan to _____

Today I'm grateful for

Draw, write, create

Day ___

Today's goal

I struggled with

I succeeded in

Instead of drinking, I ___

Tomorrow I plan to ___

Today I'm grateful for

Relax and colour

Day ___

Today's goal

I struggled with

I succeeded in

Instead of drinking, I _____

Tomorrow I plan to _____

Today I'm grateful for

Doodle and plan

Day ___

Today's goal

```
┌─────────────────────────────────────────┐
│                                         │
│                                         │
│                                         │
└─────────────────────────────────────────┘
```

I struggled with

I succeeded in

Instead of drinking, I _____

_____

_____

_____

_____

_____

Tomorrow I plan to _____

_____

_____

Today I'm grateful for

```
┌─────────────────────────────────────────┐
│                                         │
│                                         │
│                                         │
└─────────────────────────────────────────┘
```

Day ___

Today's goal

+--+
| |
| |
| |
+--+

I struggled with   *I succeeded in*

+------------------------+   +------------------------+
+------------------------+   +------------------------+

Instead of drinking, I _____

_____

_____

_____

_____

_____

_____

Tomorrow I plan to _____

_____

_____

_____

Today I'm grateful for

+--+
| |
| |
| |
+--+

Weekly Reflection

_____
_____
_____
_____
_____
_____
_____
_____
_____
_____
_____
_____
_____
_____
_____
_____
_____
_____
_____
_____

> If we are facing in the right direction all we have to
> do is keep on walking.
>
> _Zen proverb_

My diet and exercise plan

My daily supplements

Vitamins	Minerals	Superfoods

Weight loss tracker

Week 1
Start

Week 2

Week 3

Week 4

Week 5

Week 6

Week 7

Week 8

Week 9

Week 10

Week 11

Week 12

Week 13

Week 14

Day 100

Mocktail of the week

Bellini Innocente

This version of the classic 1930s peach and champagne cocktail has all of the elegance and none of the alcohol. Make sure you use dry cider (rather than a sparkling apple juice) to balance the sweetness of the peach.

100 ml peach juice (or puree, if peaches are in season)
100 ml alcohol-free dry cider

Pour the peach juice into a champagne flute and add the cider. Garnish with a peach slice.

Day ___

Today's goal

I struggled with

I succeeded in

Instead of drinking, I _____

Tomorrow I plan to _____

Today I'm grateful for

After one month

By then end of your first month without alcohol, your liver fat will have reduced by around 20%, allowing the liver to flush toxins from your system more efficiently. Your cholesterol will have dropped 5%, reducing your risk of heart disease, and your blood sugar will have dropped by around 16%, greatly reducing your risk of Type II diabetes. A month alcohol-free has a very positive impact on your long-term health.

You will be looking better on the outside, too. Your skin will look younger, fresher, and more radiant. Cell renewal will be improved and premature skin ageing prevented. You will have more energy, and the improvement in your liver function will keep your hormones balanced and protect you from infections.

Any craving for alcohol that you now experience will be psychological rather than physical, so stay focused on the benefits.

How I'm feeling

_____

_____

_____

_____

_____

_____

_____

Day ___

Today's goal

I struggled with   *I succeeded in*

Instead of drinking, I _____

_____

_____

_____

_____

_____

Tomorrow I plan to _____

_____

_____

Today I'm grateful for

Relax and colour

Day ___

Today's goal

I struggled with

I succeeded in

Instead of drinking, I _____

_____

_____

_____

_____

_____

Tomorrow I plan to _____

_____

_____

Today I'm grateful for

Day ___

Today's goal

```
┌─────────────────────────────────────┐
│                                     │
│                                     │
│                                     │
└─────────────────────────────────────┘
```

I struggled with   *I succeeded in*

```
┌──────────────────┐    ┌──────────────────┐
│                  │    │                  │
│                  │    │                  │
│                  │    │                  │
└──────────────────┘    └──────────────────┘
```

Instead of drinking, I _____

_____

_____

_____

_____

_____

_____

Tomorrow I plan to _____

_____

_____

_____

Today I'm grateful for

```
┌─────────────────────────────────────┐
│                                     │
│                                     │
│                                     │
└─────────────────────────────────────┘
```

Day ___

Today's goal

I struggled with

I succeeded in

Instead of drinking, I _____

_____
_____
_____
_____
_____
_____

Tomorrow I plan to _____

_____
_____
_____

Today I'm grateful for

Doodle and plan

Day ___

Today's goal

I struggled with

I succeeded in

Instead of drinking, I _____

Tomorrow I plan to _____

Today I'm grateful for

Day ___

Today's goal

I struggled with

I succeeded in

Instead of drinking, I ___

Tomorrow I plan to ___

Today I'm grateful for

Weekly Reflection

_____
_____
_____
_____
_____
_____
_____
_____
_____
_____
_____
_____
_____
_____
_____
_____
_____
_____
_____
_____

> If things go wrong, don't go down with them.
> _Roger Babson_

Monthy mood tracker

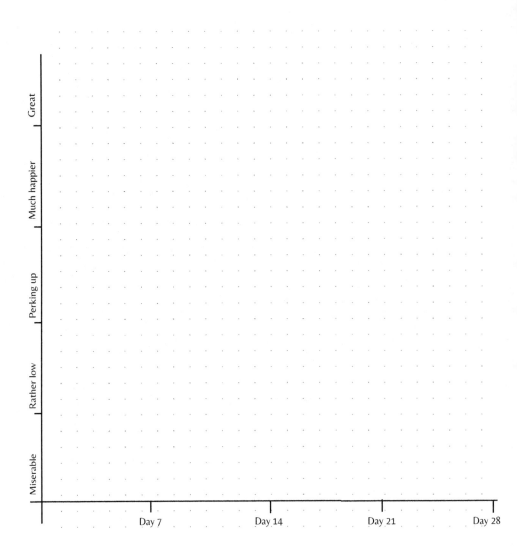

Great

Much happier

Perking up

Rather low

Miserable

Day 7   Day 14   Day 21   Day 28

Day ___

Today's goal

I struggled with

I succeeded in

Instead of drinking, I _____

_____

_____

_____

_____

_____

_____

Tomorrow I plan to _____

_____

_____

_____

Today I'm grateful for

Mocktail of the week

Fur of the Cat

This zesty citrus mocktail is perfect for a summer brunch. You don't need that "hair of the dog" these days, so perk up your morning with a "fur of the cat" instead!

100 ml grapefruit juice
100 ml cranberry juice
A dash of Angostura bitters
50 ml sparkling water
Lime

Combine the juices and pour into a tall glass filled with ice. Add a dash of Angostura and top up with sparkling water. Garnish with a slice of lime.

Day ___

Today's goal

I struggled with

I succeeded in

Instead of drinking, I _____

_____

_____

_____

_____

_____

_____

Tomorrow I plan to _____

_____

_____

_____

Today I'm grateful for

Day ___

Today's goal

_____

I struggled with   *I succeeded in*

Instead of drinking, I _____

_____

_____

_____

_____

_____

Tomorrow I plan to _____

_____

_____

Today I'm grateful for

_____

Draw, write, create

Doodle and plan

Day ___

Today's goal

I struggled with

I succeeded in

Instead of drinking, I _____

_____

_____

_____

_____

_____

Tomorrow I plan to _____

_____

_____

_____

Today I'm grateful for

Day ___

Today's goal

I struggled with

I succeeded in

Instead of drinking, I _____

_____

_____

_____

_____

_____

Tomorrow I plan to _____

_____

_____

_____

Today I'm grateful for

Day ___

Today's goal

I struggled with   **I succeeded in**

Instead of drinking, I _____

_____

_____

_____

_____

_____

_____

Tomorrow I plan to _____

_____

_____

Today I'm grateful for

Day ___

Today's goal

I struggled with

I succeeded in

Instead of drinking, I _____

_____

_____

_____

_____

_____

Tomorrow I plan to _____

_____

_____

_____

Today I'm grateful for

Weekly Reflection

> Courage isn't having the strength to go on - it's going on when you don't have the strength.
>
> *Napoleon Bonaparte*

Relax and colour

Day ___

Today's goal

```

```

I struggled with   I succeeded in

```

```
```

```

Instead of drinking, I _____

_____

_____

_____

_____

_____

Tomorrow I plan to _____

_____

_____

Today I'm grateful for

```

```

Mocktail of the week

Sunrise

Inspired by the classic tequila sunrise, this mocktail uses grenadine for flavour and colour. You can buy grenadine syrup or easily make it yourself by combining equal parts sugar and pomegranate juice and simmering over a gentle heat, stirring until the sugar is dissolved and the mixture slightly thickened. Pour into a heatproof bottle, allow to cool and add a few splashes of orange flower water. An essential ingredient for your mocktail bar!

The key to success with your Sunrise mocktail is to avoid stirring it, so that you don't disturb the wonderfully graduated sunrise colours.

200 ml orange juice
20 ml grenadine syrup
Mint

Add a handful of ice to a tall glass and fill with orange juice. Pour over the grenadine syrup: it will sink to the bottom, gradually rising up to give a sunrise burst to your mocktail. Garnish with a sprig of mint.

Day ___

Today's goal

I struggled with

I succeeded in

Instead of drinking, I _____

Tomorrow I plan to _____

Today I'm grateful for

Day ___

Today's goal

I struggled with

I succeeded in

Instead of drinking, I _____

_____

_____

_____

_____

_____

Tomorrow I plan to _____

_____

_____

Today I'm grateful for

Day ___

Today's goal

I struggled with

I succeeded in

Instead of drinking, I ___

Tomorrow I plan to ___

Today I'm grateful for

Day ___

Today's goal

```

```

I struggled with   *I succeeded in*

Instead of drinking, I _____

_____

_____

_____

_____

_____

Tomorrow I plan to _____

_____

_____

Today I'm grateful for

```

```

Draw, write, create

Doodle and plan

Day ___

Today's goal

I struggled with

I succeeded in

Instead of drinking, I _____

Tomorrow I plan to _____

Today I'm grateful for

Day ___

Today's goal

I struggled with   *I succeeded in*

Instead of drinking, I _____
_____
_____
_____
_____
_____

Tomorrow I plan to _____
_____
_____

Today I'm grateful for

Weekly Reflection

> When everything feels like an uphill struggle, just
> think of the view from the top.
>
> *Anon.*

Mocktail of the week

Virgin Pina Colada

In this mocktail, the rum base of the traditional pina colada is suggested by vanilla and nutmeg, which provide the aromatic notes found in a typical dark rum.

120 ml pineapple juice
60 ml coconut milk (shake to mix well)
Juice of one lime
A few drops of vanilla essence
A sprinkle of grated nutmeg

Blend the ingredients with a handful of ice, pour, and garnish with mint or a pineapple wedge.

Day ___

Today's goal

```
┌─────────────────────────────────────────────┐
│                                             │
│                                             │
│                                             │
└─────────────────────────────────────────────┘
```

I struggled with   I succeeded in

```
┌──────────────────────┐    ┌──────────────────────┐
│                      │    │                      │
│                      │    │                      │
│                      │    │                      │
└──────────────────────┘    └──────────────────────┘
```

Instead of drinking, I _____

_____

_____

_____

_____

_____

_____

Tomorrow I plan to _____

_____

_____

_____

Today I'm grateful for

```
┌─────────────────────────────────────────────┐
│                                             │
│                                             │
│                                             │
└─────────────────────────────────────────────┘
```

Day ___

Today's goal

[ ]

I struggled with   *I succeeded in*

[ ]   [ ]

Instead of drinking, I _____
_____
_____
_____
_____
_____
_____

Tomorrow I plan to _____
_____
_____
_____

Today I'm grateful for

[ ]

Day ___

Today's goal

Instead of drinking, I _____

_____

_____

_____

_____

_____

_____

Tomorrow I plan to _____

_____

_____

Today I'm grateful for

Day ___

Today's goal

I struggled with   *I succeeded in*

Instead of drinking, I _____

_____

_____

_____

_____

_____

Tomorrow I plan to _____

_____

_____

Today I'm grateful for

Day ___

Today's goal

I struggled with

I succeeded in

Instead of drinking, I _____

_____

_____

_____

_____

_____

_____

Tomorrow I plan to _____

_____

_____

Today I'm grateful for

Doodle and plan

Day ___

Today's goal

I struggled with

I succeeded in

Instead of drinking, I ___

Tomorrow I plan to ___

Today I'm grateful for

Day ___

Today's goal

[ ]

I struggled with   *I succeeded in*

[ ]   [ ]

Instead of drinking, I _____

_____
_____
_____
_____
_____

Tomorrow I plan to _____

_____
_____

Today I'm grateful for

[ ]

Weekly Reflection

_____
_____
_____
_____
_____
_____
_____
_____
_____
_____
_____
_____
_____
_____
_____
_____
_____
_____
_____
_____
_____
_____
_____
_____

> Be stronger than your strongest excuse.
> _Anon._

Mocktail of the week

Shirley Temple

This non-alcoholic drink was invented by a barman in Beverley Hills for the young Shirley Temple. Naturally, with the child star being well under drinking age, he swerved the alcohol and in the process created a classic mocktail.

45 ml grenadine
180 ml ginger ale (I like Fever Tree as it has a complex ginger flavour and isn't too sweet)
Lemon or maraschino cherry

Pour the grenadine into a tall glass filled with ice. Top with the ginger ale and garnish with a slice of lemon or a maraschino cherry.

Day ___

Today's goal

I struggled with   I succeeded in

Instead of drinking, I _____

_____

_____

_____

_____

_____

_____

Tomorrow I plan to _____

_____

_____

Today I'm grateful for

Day ___

Today's goal

I struggled with

I succeeded in

Instead of drinking, I _____

Tomorrow I plan to _____

Today I'm grateful for

Day ___

Today's goal

[ ]

I struggled with

[ ]

I succeeded in

[ ]

Instead of drinking, I ___

___
___
___
___
___

Tomorrow I plan to ___

___
___

Today I'm grateful for

[ ]

Day ___

Today's goal

I struggled with

I succeeded in

Instead of drinking, I _____

_____

_____

_____

_____

_____

_____

Tomorrow I plan to _____

_____

_____

Today I'm grateful for

Day ___

Today's goal

I struggled with

I succeeded in

Instead of drinking, I _____

Tomorrow I plan to _____

Today I'm grateful for

Relax and colour

Day ___

Today's goal

I struggled with

I succeeded in

Instead of drinking, I _____

Tomorrow I plan to _____

Today I'm grateful for

Day ___

Today's goal

I struggled with   *I succeeded in*

Instead of drinking, I _____
_____
_____
_____
_____
_____

Tomorrow I plan to _____
_____
_____

Today I'm grateful for

Weekly Reflection

The days you are most uncomfortable are the days
you learn the most about yourself.

Anon.

Monthy mood tracker

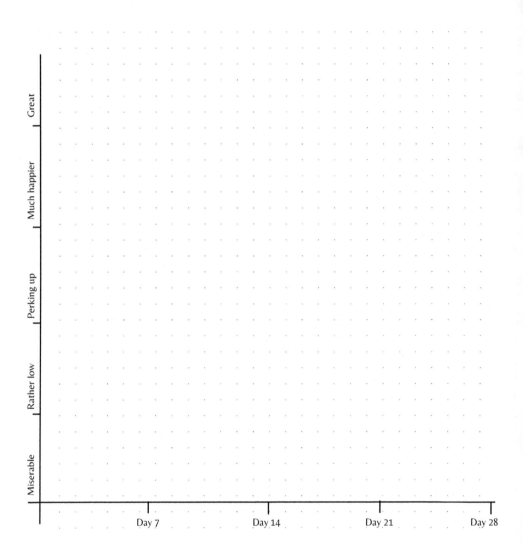

Day ___

Today's goal

I struggled with

I succeeded in

Instead of drinking, I _____

_____

_____

_____

_____

_____

_____

Tomorrow I plan to _____

_____

_____

_____

Today I'm grateful for

Mocktail of the week

Botanicals and Tonic

Botanical distillations are a great gin substitute (Seedlip is the best known, but there are numerous others). Nothing could be simpler than this mocktail, and it's hard to tell it isn't actually a gin and tonic.

50 ml Seedlip (or other botanical elixir)
Tonic water (I like Fever Tree Elderflower to add to the complexity of the botanical flavours)
Angostura bitters
Lemon

Pour a measure of your choice of gin-style botantical over the ice and top up with tonic water. Add a splash of Angostura and garnish with a slice of lemon.

Day ___

Today's goal

I struggled with

I succeeded in

Instead of drinking, I ___

Tomorrow I plan to ___

Today I'm grateful for

Day ___

Today's goal

I struggled with

I succeeded in

Instead of drinking, I ___

Tomorrow I plan to ___

Today I'm grateful for

Day ___

Today's goal

I struggled with

I succeeded in

Instead of drinking, I _____

Tomorrow I plan to _____

Today I'm grateful for

Day ___

Today's goal

I struggled with   *I succeeded in*

Instead of drinking, I _____
_____
_____
_____
_____
_____
_____

Tomorrow I plan to _____
_____
_____
_____

Today I'm grateful for

Day ___

Today's goal

```



```

I struggled with

```


```

I succeeded in

```


```

Instead of drinking, I _____

_____

_____

_____

_____

_____

Tomorrow I plan to _____

_____

_____

_____

Today I'm grateful for

```


```

Day ___

Today's goal

I struggled with

I succeeded in

Instead of drinking, I _____

_____

_____

_____

_____

_____

Tomorrow I plan to _____

_____

_____

_____

Today I'm grateful for

Weekly Reflection

_____

_____

_____

_____

_____

_____

_____

_____

_____

_____

_____

_____

_____

_____

_____

_____

_____

_____

_____

_____

_____

Fall down seven times, stand up eight.
Japanese proverb

Draw, write, create

Day ___

Today's goal

I struggled with   *I succeeded in*

Instead of drinking, I _____

_____

_____

_____

_____

_____

Tomorrow I plan to _____

_____

_____

Today I'm grateful for

Mocktail of the week

Stormy Night

The wintery spices give this mocktail a warming and aromatic glow. Make the spiced syrup in advance and keep it in a container in the fridge. It will last a week or so.

200 g muscovado sugar
200 ml water
1 cinnamon stick
1 star anise
1 whole nutmeg
4 cardamom pods
500 ml good quality ginger beer
A squeeze of lemon

To make the spiced syrup, combine the sugar and water, add the spices and simmer gently for 20 minutes. Leave the mixture to infuse overnight at room temperature, and strain the next day. Store in a sealed container.

To make your Stormy Night, add a few ice cubes to the glass, and pour over 30 ml of the spiced syrup. Top with ginger beer and a squeeze of lemon.

Day ___

Today's goal

I struggled with

I succeeded in

Instead of drinking, I _____

Tomorrow I plan to _____

Today I'm grateful for

Day ___

Today's goal

I struggled with   *I succeeded in*

Instead of drinking, I _____

_____

_____

_____

_____

_____

Tomorrow I plan to _____

_____

_____

Today I'm grateful for

Day ___

Today's goal

I struggled with

I succeeded in

Instead of drinking, I _____

Tomorrow I plan to _____

Today I'm grateful for

Day ___

Today's goal

I struggled with   I succeeded in

Instead of drinking, I _____

_____

_____

_____

_____

_____

Tomorrow I plan to _____

_____

_____

Today I'm grateful for

Day ___

Today's goal

I struggled with

I succeeded in

Instead of drinking, I _____

Tomorrow I plan to _____

Today I'm grateful for

Day ___

Today's goal

I struggled with

I succeeded in

Instead of drinking, I _____

Tomorrow I plan to _____

Today I'm grateful for

Weekly Reflection

_____

_____

_____

_____

_____

_____

_____

_____

_____

_____

_____

_____

_____

_____

_____

_____

_____

_____

_____

_____

_____

_____

> Don't judge each day by the harvest you reap but by
> the seeds that you plant.
>
> _Robert Louis Stevenson_

Mocktail of the week

Nojito

This delicious take on the mojito is full of the fresh flavours of mint, lime and elderflower, and lightly sparkling with bubbles.

A small handful of mint leaves
Juice of two limes
30 ml elderflower cordial
60 ml apple juice
A drop or two of rum extract
Sparkling mineral water or soda water

Gently pummel 12 or so mint leaves (with a wooden spoon or a pestle) in a jug to extract the oils and release the aroma. You should aim to soften rather than crush them. Add the apple juice, elderflower cordial, lime juice and rum extract to the jug and mix. Pour the mint and juices into glasses with some crushed ice and top up with the sparkling water. Garnish with a sprig of mint and a wedge of lime.

Day ___

Today's goal

I struggled with

I succeeded in

Instead of drinking, I _____

_____

_____

_____

_____

_____

Tomorrow I plan to _____

_____

_____

Today I'm grateful for

Day ___

Today's goal

I struggled with

I succeeded in

Instead of drinking, I _____

_____

_____

_____

_____

_____

_____

Tomorrow I plan to _____

_____

_____

_____

Today I'm grateful for

Day ___

Today's goal

I struggled with

I succeeded in

Instead of drinking, I _____

_____

_____

_____

_____

_____

Tomorrow I plan to _____

_____

_____

Today I'm grateful for

Day ___

Today's goal

I struggled with   *I succeeded in*

Instead of drinking, I _____

_____

_____

_____

_____

_____

Tomorrow I plan to _____

_____

_____

Today I'm grateful for

Day ___

Today's goal

I struggled with

I succeeded in

Instead of drinking, I _____

Tomorrow I plan to _____

Today I'm grateful for

Doodle and plan

Day ___

Today's goal

I struggled with   *I succeeded in*

Instead of drinking, I _____

_____
_____
_____
_____
_____
_____

Tomorrow I plan to _____

_____
_____
_____

Today I'm grateful for

Day ___

Today's goal

I struggled with

I succeeded in

Instead of drinking, I _____

_____
_____
_____
_____
_____
_____

Tomorrow I plan to _____

_____
_____
_____

Today I'm grateful for

Weekly Reflection

> The best way to predict your future is to create it.
> *Abraham Lincoln*

Mocktail of the week

Sparkling Ruby

Pomegranate juice has a wonderfully rich colour and flavour –
and is loaded with healthy anti-oxidants. I recommend buying
your pomegranate juice already extracted and helpfully bottled,
as preparing it from the fruit can leave your kitchen looking
like a crime scene.

100 ml pomegranate juice
100 ml sparkling mineral water
2 limes

Squeeze the limes and add to the pomegranate juice. Pour
the juices over ice in a tall glass. Add the sparkling water, and
garnish with a slice of lime and some pomegranate arils (you
could use icecube arils, if you have some left over from your
Rosy Glow).

Day ___

Today's goal

I struggled with

I succeeded in

Instead of drinking, I _____

Tomorrow I plan to _____

Today I'm grateful for

After three months

Congratulations! You've nearly completed your 100 days alcohol-free. It's a great, and potentially life-changing, achievement.

After three months without drinking, you have reduced your risk of cancer. Alcohol is a major carcinogen and directly linked to seven different kinds of cancer, including mouth and breast cancer. You have also reduced your risk of stroke, heart disease, high blood pressure, diabetes, depression, anxiety, and insomnia.

You will have more energy, sleep better, and be more focused and productive. Your moods will be more stable. You will have lost weight and saved money.

People who reach the 3 month mark are more likely to continue not drinking or to moderate their drinking significantly in the future. After all, now you feel and look great!

How I'm feeling

Day ___

Today's goal

I struggled with   *I succeeded in*

Instead of drinking, I _____

_____

_____

_____

_____

_____

Tomorrow I plan to _____

_____

_____

Today I'm grateful for

Draw, write, create

Day ___

Today's goal

I struggled with   I succeeded in

Instead of drinking, I _____

_____

_____

_____

_____

_____

_____

Tomorrow I plan to _____

_____

_____

_____

Today I'm grateful for

Day ___

Today's goal

I struggled with   *I succeeded in*

Instead of drinking, I _____
_____
_____
_____
_____
_____
_____

Tomorrow I plan to _____
_____
_____

Today I'm grateful for

Day ___

Today's goal

I struggled with

I succeeded in

Instead of drinking, I _____

_____

_____

_____

_____

_____

_____

Tomorrow I plan to _____

_____

_____

_____

Today I'm grateful for

Doodle and plan

Day ___

Today's goal

I struggled with

I succeeded in

Instead of drinking, I _____

Tomorrow I plan to _____

Today I'm grateful for

Day ___

Today's goal

> ┌─────────────────────────────────────┐
> │   │
> │   │
> │   │
> └─────────────────────────────────────┘

I struggled with   *I succeeded in*

> ┌──────────────────┐   ┌──────────────────┐
> │   │   │   │
> │   │   │   │
> │   │   │   │
> └──────────────────┘   └──────────────────┘

Instead of drinking, I _____

_____

_____

_____

_____

_____

Tomorrow I plan to _____

_____

_____

Today I'm grateful for

> ┌─────────────────────────────────────┐
> │   │
> │   │
> │   │
> └─────────────────────────────────────┘

Weekly Reflection

Waking up sober is the first gift of every day.
Anon.

Monthy mood tracker

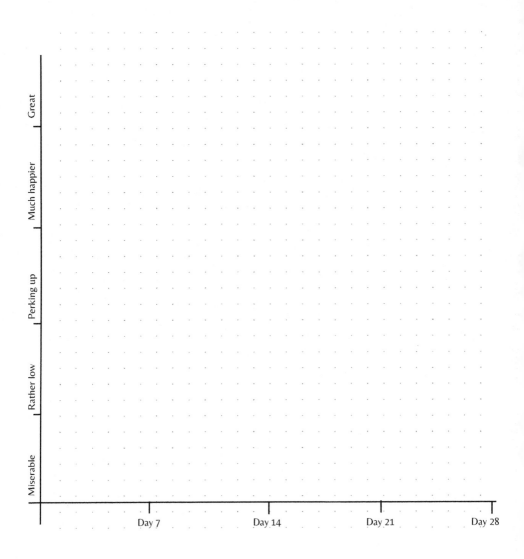

Great

Much happier

Perking up

Rather low

Miserable

Day 7　　　Day 14　　　Day 21　　　Day 28

Day ___

Today's goal

I struggled with

I succeeded in

Instead of drinking, I ___

Tomorrow I plan to ___

Today I'm grateful for

Mocktail of the week

French Kiss

This reminds me a bit of a champagne cocktail. I've always thought it a shame to mess with France's finest product (now off limits, but still deserving of respect), and no champagne has been harmed in the creation of this drink.

Juice of two lemons
A few dashes of Angostura bitters
500 ml premium tonic water (I like Fever Tree elderflower tonic with this one)

Combine the lemon juice and bitters and top up with tonic water. Serve in a champagne flute and garnish with rock candy swizzle sticks for effect and a touch of sweetness. You can use a little sugar to take the edge off the lemon if you don't have the swizzle sticks.

Day ___

Today's goal

I struggled with

I succeeded in

Instead of drinking, I _____

Tomorrow I plan to _____

Today I'm grateful for

Doodle and plan

Day ___

Today's goal

I struggled with

I succeeded in

Instead of drinking, I ___

Tomorrow I plan to ___

Today I'm grateful for

Day ___

Today's goal

I struggled with

I succeeded in

Instead of drinking, I _____

_____

_____

_____

_____

_____

_____

Tomorrow I plan to_____

_____

_____

_____

Today I'm grateful for

Day ___

Today's goal

I struggled with

I succeeded in

Instead of drinking, I ___

Tomorrow I plan to ___

Today I'm grateful for

Day ___

Today's goal

I struggled with   *I succeeded in*

Instead of drinking, I _____

_____

_____

_____

_____

_____

Tomorrow I plan to _____

_____

_____

Today I'm grateful for

Draw, write, create

Day ___

Today's goal

I struggled with

I succeeded in

Instead of drinking, I _____

Tomorrow I plan to _____

Today I'm grateful for

Weekly Reflection

Always remember that the future comes one day
at a time.

Dean Acheson

Mocktail of the week

Pointsettia au Naturel

This is my version of a festive champagne-style cocktail which traditionally combines a sparkling wine such champagne, cava or prosecco, with cranberry juice and Cointreau. Non-alcoholic sparkling wines are now relatively easy to come by, and though they are rather sweet and lacking body on their own, they work perfectly in a mocktail. The orange juice stands in for the Cointreau.

40 ml orange juice
160 ml cranberry juice (preferably unsweetened)
Non-alcoholic sparkling white wine (Nosecco is surprisingly good)

Mix the orange and cranberry juices and pour into two champagne flutes. Top with the chilled Nosecco or other non-alcoholic sparkling wine.

Day ___

Today's goal

I struggled with

I succeeded in

Instead of drinking, I ___

Tomorrow I plan to ___

Today I'm grateful for

Day ___

Today's goal

I struggled with

I succeeded in

Instead of drinking, I ___

Tomorrow I plan to ___

Today I'm grateful for

Day ___

Today's goal

I struggled with

I succeeded in

Instead of drinking, I _____

Tomorrow I plan to _____

Today I'm grateful for

Day ___

Today's goal

```
[                                    ]
```

I struggled with   *I succeeded in*

Instead of drinking, I _____

_____

_____

_____

_____

_____

_____

Tomorrow I plan to _____

_____

_____

Today I'm grateful for

Day ___

Today's goal

I struggled with   *I succeeded in*

Instead of drinking, I _____

_____

_____

_____

_____

_____

Tomorrow I plan to _____

_____

_____

Today I'm grateful for

Doodle and plan

Day ___

Today's goal

I struggled with

I succeeded in

Instead of drinking, I _____

Tomorrow I plan to _____

Today I'm grateful for

Day ___

Today's goal

I struggled with   *I succeeded in*

Instead of drinking, I _____
_____
_____
_____
_____
_____

Tomorrow I plan to _____
_____
_____

Today I'm grateful for

Weekly Reflection

_____

_____

_____

_____

_____

_____

_____

_____

_____

_____

_____

_____

_____

_____

_____

_____

_____

_____

_____

_____

_____

I am in the process of becoming the best version
of myself.

Anon.

Day ___

Today's goal

I struggled with   I succeeded in

Instead of drinking, I _____
_____
_____
_____
_____
_____
_____

Tomorrow I plan to _____
_____
_____

Today I'm grateful for

Day ___

Today's goal

I struggled with | I succeeded in

Instead of drinking, I _____

Tomorrow I plan to _____

Today I'm grateful for

Savings tracker

Work out your previous average weekly spend on alcohol. Include wine, beer and spirits purchased for drinking at home, as well as any typical spending in pubs, restaurants and clubs.

Keep a cumulative record of what you are NOT spending week by week and watch your savings mount up!

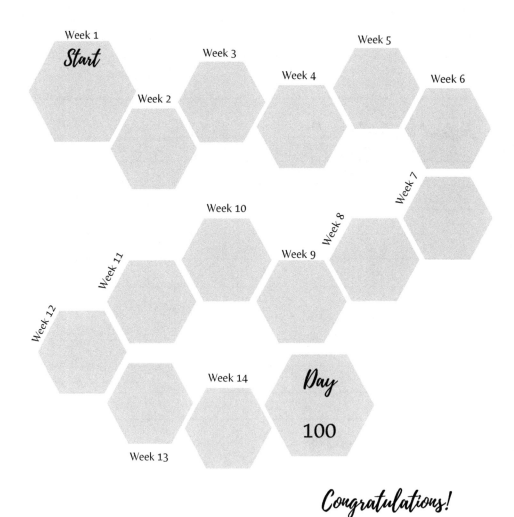

Congratulations!

Final Reflection

What I've learnt _____

_____

_____

_____

What I've achieved _____

_____

_____

_____

Looking ahead _____

_____

_____

_____

Hopes and aspirations _____

_____

_____

_____

_____

And finally, I'm grateful for

Notes

Printed in Great Britain
by Amazon

42812775R00098